MW00947606

LOOK AT THE BOY THAT LOOKS LIKE A FOX

for JAM

...never jelly

WRITTEN BY MARCUS KAHLE McCANN

ILLUSTRATED BY ZITA VARGA

POCKETS OF...
PUBLISHING

LOOK AT ME RUN

BECAUSE I'M

FAST AS A FOX.

SO SWIFT LIKE A FOX.

I'M QUICK AS A FOX.

LOOK AT ME
J U M P
BECAUSE
I'M SPRY LIKE A FOX.
JUST AS FLEET AS A FOX.

I'M LITHE LIKE A FOX.

LOOK AT ME REASON

BECAUSE I'M
KEEN AS A
FOX.

VERY WISE
LIKE A FOX

I'M SLY
AS A FOX.

NOW LOOK
AT ME,
AND SEE THAT
YOU SEE
THAT I AM
NOT A FOX

BUT A BOY,
INDEED,
A YOUNG
MAN

OF A CERTAIN STATURE AND POISE

WITH ALL THE
SAME FEAUTRES
AS OTHER
SUCH BOYS.

NOW LET ME
BE CLEAR,

THESE ARE
NOT PAWS
THAT I HAVE

BUT TWO BEAUTIFUL FEET
AND TWO CAPABLE HANDS

...THAT JUST SO
HAPPEN
TO BE CLEVERLY
HIDDEN

BY THESE FUZZY BLACK SOCKS
AND THESE BLACK WOOLEN MITTENS.

AND I ASSURE
YOU THIS COAT
(THAT IS RED
LIKE BRIGHT
PASSION)

I WEAR ONLY
FOR WARMTH!

...AND
SOMETIMES
FOR

FASHION.

MY EARS ARE NOT POINTED.

MY TEETH ARE
NOT
SHARP.

MY TAIL IS NOT BUSHY

AND IT'S RARE THAT I BARK!

NO,
I AM
NOT A
fox
I DON'T PLOT
OR CONNIVE;

I AM ONLY A MAN WITH
MISCHIEVOUS EYES

BUT NEVER-YOU-MIND
THESE MISCHIEVOUS EYES.
FOR IF YOU LOOK DEEP BEHIND THEM

YOU WILL FIND
NOTHING BUT KINDNESS.

BECAUSE I'M SOFT AS A FOX.

TRULY WARM LIKE A FOX.

I'M LIGHT

AS A FOX.

LOOK AT ME
BECAUSE I
LOOK
LIKE A FOX.

JUST ENOUGH LIKE A FOX.

I'M A BOY
LIKE A FOX.

A LITTLE HELP WITH WORDS

SWIFT • adjective Fast. Moving or able to move quickly.

SPRY • adjective Full of energy.

FLEET • adjective Fast. Swift. (As a noun, it can also mean a large group of boats or planes or trucks, but that definition wouldn't make much sense in this book, would it?)

LITHE • adjective Flexible. Bends easily.

KEEN • adjective Sharp (If a person is described as sharp, it means they are smart or clever. They have a sharp mind.)

WISE • adjective Knowing the right thing to say or do.

SLY • adjective Secretly clever.

STATURE • noun Height.

POISE • noun Balance. A confident way of carrying oneself.

CAPABLE • adjective Having skill or ability.

RED • There is a kind of fox called the Red Fox, but it actually looks more orange than red, which is why our foxboy describes his orange coat as red... in case you were wondering.

PLOT • verb To make a plan (especially a plan to make trouble).

CONNIVE • verb To make a plan. To work together with trouble-makers in secret.

MISCHIEVOUS • adjective Showing a fondness for causing trouble (often in a playful way). (Pronounced 'mis chivus' or 'mis chee vee us'. Feel free to use whichever pronunciation you like the sound of best; you can even mix and match!)

ABOUT THE AUTHOR

Kahle is an award-winning playwright, lyricist, and entertainer currently working with Mildly Fearsome Films, a production company based in Los Angeles where he lives with his wife, Becky. Kahle firmly believes that if Writers write at the top of their intelligence, Readers will read at the top of theirs and that if they read or hear enough stories that are "over their heads," it won't be long before they have taller heads... not literally... Kahle does NOT promote the idea that literacy leads to weird cranial mutations.

ABOUT THE ILLUSTRATOR

Zita is a Hungarian artist and graphic designer, living with her partner, Daniel. She believes in the magical power of the visual arts to enlighten, inspire, and empower; drawing (no pun intended) her inspiration from her own childhood as well as her friends and their children and the details of the world they share. If you would like to see more of her work, you can do so at zizudraws.com.

For more information about Pockets of... Publishing
and our other books please visit us at

www.pocketsofbooks.com

CPSIA information can be obtained
at www.ICGtesting.com
Printed in the USA
BVHW020152231220
596332BV00012B/88